Year 4

Fiction & Poetry Writing

by Heather Bell

Introduction

Photocopiable Fiction and Poetry Writing for Year 4 is designed as an aid to the busy classroom teacher planning extended writing activities for the Literacy Strategy.

The objectives for each activity are taken directly from the National Literacy Strategy.
The author has chosen a selection of passages from different genres by leading children's writers, in the belief that good literature 'speaks' and is an excellent stimulus for writing.

Writing frames are included, to aid children when they are planning their writing. For those children who struggle to think up ideas, or who have special needs, there are writing support sheets for many of the activities.

Topical Resources, P.O. Box 329, Broughton, Preston, Lancashire. PR3 5LT

Topical Resources publishes a range of Educational Materials for use in Primary Schools and Pre-School Nurseries and Playgroups.

For the latest catalogue:
Tel 01772 863158
Fax 01772 866153
e.mail: sales@topical-resources.co.uk
Visit our Website at:
www.topical-resources.co.uk

Copyright © 2002 Heather Bell
Illustrated by John Hutchinson, Paul Sealey & Andy Short

Typeset by Paul Sealey Illustration & Design, 3 Wentworth Drive, Thornton, Lancashire.

Printed in Great Britain for 'Topical Resources', Publishers of Educational Materials, P.O. Box 329, Broughton, Preston, Lancashire PR3 5LT by T. Snape & Company Limited, Boltons Court, Preston, Lancashire.

First Published September 2002

ISBN 1 872977 69 3

Acknowledgments

Thanks are due to the following authors and publishers for permission to reproduce short extracts:

'Stig of the Dump' by Clive King and 'Cider with Rosie' by Laurie Lee with permission of The Penguin Group (UK).

'Matilda', 'The Witches' and 'Charlie and the Chocolate Factory' by Roald Dahl with permission of David Higham Associates'

'Friend or Foe' by Michael Morpurgo

'My Naughty Little Sister' by Dorothy Edwards.

'The Owl who was afraid of the Dark' by Jill Tomlinson and 'What is Red' from 'Hailstones and Halibut Bones' by Mary Gibbons O'Neill with permission of Egmont Books Ltd.

'The Borrowers' by Mary Norton with permisson of The Orion Publishing Group Ltd.

'A Smuggler's Song' by Rudyard Kipling with permission of A.P. Watt Ltd. on behalf of The National Trust for Places of Historical Interest or Natural Beauty.

'Grandfather Clock' from Rhyme and Reason written by Sylvia Turner with permission of Harper Collins Publishers Ltd.

The publishers have endeavoured to trace the copyright holders of all the texts in this publication. If we have unwittingly infringed copyright, we sincerely apologise and will be pleased, on being satisfied as to the owner's title, to pay an appropriate fee as if we had been able to obtain prior permission.

Contents

Planning Stories

Planning Stories

National Literacy Strategy Year 4 Term 1:

To use different ways of planning stories e.g. using brainstorming, notes and diagrams.

Brainstorming Ideas for a Story

Look at the photocopiable example sheet 'Winter Holiday' with the children. Explain to them that this is an example of brainstorming ideas for a story about a Winter Holiday. Explain that it is important that when doing this, the main headings should be found first, then put down ideas related to these headings. If struggling for ideas, the children should always ask themselves the questions Who, What, Where, Why and When to encourage the flow of ideas. To see if the children have grasped this type of planning, they should brainstorm ideas for a story with the title 'A Summer Holiday'.

Using Notes to Plan a Story

Look at the photocopiable example sheet on notes as a form of planning. After reading these through with the children, bring out the idea that this is a brief outline of the story and need not be written in sentences; words and phrases will do. The children should use this form of planning for a story with the title, 'The Old Junk Shop'.

Using Diagrams to Plan a Story

Look at the photocopiable example of 'Journey into Another World'. Explain that this is planning a story in a diagrammatic way. The arrows show how each stage of the story progresses. The children should create a story plan in a diagrammatic way for a story with the title 'Journey into a Magic Land'.

Planning a Story

Example 1
Brainstorming

How We Got There
By car, airport, plane, journey, long, boring, exciting, new country, arrival.

Where We Stayed
France, in mountains, hotel, friendly, lots of other families.

Weather
Snowy, cold, fine powdery snow, bright sunny days, deep snow drifts, snowballs.

Title: Winter Holiday

How We Spent Our Time
Up early in the morning, chair lift to mountain ski runs, sledging, evenings – disco in hotel, eating, talking to new friends.

Big Event
Dad messing about on ski lift, falls off! Broken leg, brought down mountain in air ambulance, hospital.

Journey Home
Holiday cut short, Dad in wheel chair, has to be lifted on/ off plane, Mum says, "Serves him right for messing about!", everyone signs his plaster.

Planning a Story

Example 2
Using Notes

Title: The Empty House!

Playing out at Grandma's - discover nearby old house - overgrown garden - high wall - huge wooden gate. Decide to explore - peer in windows – dirty - difficult to see through – inside old furniture - grandfather clock - grand piano - old pictures.

Look through another window – iron bedstead, patchwork quilt, large old-fashioned wardrobe – see cat!
Is it stuck inside house?

Decide to go in to rescue it - try to open the door - BUT… it suddenly opens – old lady appears - looks angry - asks what I want.

Say sorry - run back to Grandma's - hope I'm not in trouble.

Planning a Story

Example 3
Using a Diagram

Title: Journey into Another World

Playing football in a field near my Aunt's house - having fun – one of my cousins kicks ball through window of an old shed.

I go to investigate – ball is resting on a battered old rocking chair – begins to rock – grab ball – something strange happens.

I seem to be thrown through the air – land on grass under trees in a wood – decide to explore – see light ahead – it's a small house – I am invited in – family of squirrels who can talk – drink cup of tea and save a ginger biscuit in my pocket.

Decide I must get back home – try to find place under trees again – suddenly spot the football – pick it up – sent flying through the air – find myself back with my cousins who ask where I have been – put my hand in my pocket – find the ginger biscuit - decide not to explain.

The Cave

Barney was exploring near the edge of the chalk-pit. He had been warned of the danger that it might cave in at any minute, and of course that is just what happens….

His thoughts did those funny things they do when you bump your head and you suddenly find yourself thinking about what you had for dinner last Tuesday, all mixed up with seven times six. Barney lay with his eyes shut, waiting for his thoughts to stop being mixed up. Then he opened them.

He was lying in a kind of shelter. Looking up he could see a roof, or part of a roof, made of elder branches, a very rotten old carpet, and rusty old sheets of iron. There was a big hole, through which he must have fallen. He could see the white walls of the cliff, the trees and creepers at the top, and the sky with clouds passing over it.

Barney decided he wasn't dead. He didn't even seem to be very much hurt. He turned his head and looked around him. It was dark in this den after looking at the white chalk, and he couldn't see what sort of place it was. It seemed to be partly a cave dug into the chalk, partly a shelter built out over the mouth of the cave. There was a cool, damp smell. Woodlice and earwigs dropped from the roof where he had broken through it.

But what had happened to his legs? He couldn't sit up when he tried to. His legs wouldn't move. Perhaps I've broken them, Barney thought. What shall I do then? He looked at his legs to see if they were all right, and found they were all tangled up with creeper from the face of the cliff. Who tied me up thought Barney? He kicked his legs to try to get them free, but it was no use, there were yards of creeper trailing down from the cliff. I suppose I got tangled up when I fell, he thought. Expect I would have broken my neck if I hadn't.

He lay quiet and looked around the cave again. Now that his eyes were used to it he could see further into the dark part of the cave.

There was somebody there!
Or Something!

From Stig of the Dump by Clive King

The Cave

National Literacy Strategy Year 4 Term 1.

To plan a story identifying the stages of its telling.

Explain to the children that the passage that you are about to read is about a boy called Barney who is staying with his grandmother. Whilst Barney is exploring nearby, he goes close to the edge of a chalk-pit. The boy has been warned that it could crumble at any time and is a danger. Read the photocopiable passage to the children, and then allow them time to re-read it for themselves.

Ask the children what they think will happen next in the story. What is in the cave? Who is in the cave? Does he make friends with the boy/girl? Is the person alone in the cave or are there others living there too? Does Barney explore? Does he make friends with the cave dwellers?

Ask the children to write the events which follow on from the passage, using the title 'The Cave'. The children should use the writing frame to clarify their ideas when planning, and then write their story using paragraphs. There is a writing support sheet for those children who struggle to think up ideas of their own.

The Cave

Name: _____ **Date:** _____

Here are some words and ideas to help you. Can you add to these?

Setting
The Cave
Dark, gloomy, damp, grey walls, smell of soil, fire for heat, food-meat, fruit, animal skins to keep warm, a bed made out of heather and dry grass.

Characters in the Story
Barney:
a boy of eight or nine years old, brave, looking for an adventure, friendly, helpful, strong, wants to meet the person who lives in the cave.

Boy/ girl who lives in the cave:
Same age as Barney or a little older? Is he/she from present time or from long ago in history, perhaps a cave boy/girl? Can they understand each other? Wearing – animal skins, good at hunting. Does he/she have brothers or sisters, a mother or father?

The Cave

Writing Frame

ame: _____ **Date:** _____

The story setting:

Characters in the story:

The story begins as Barney finds himself in the cave. What is it like?

Barney realises that there is someone else in the cave. Who is it? Why is he/she there? What happens when he/she notices Barney?

Does Barney make friends with the person? Are there any other people living in the cave?

How does Barney get back home again?

People to Like and Dislike

Miss Honey

Miss Jennifer Honey was a mild and quiet person who never raised her voice and was seldom seen to smile, but there is no doubt she possessed that rare gift for being adored by every small child under her care. She seemed to understand totally the bewilderment and fear that so often overwhelms young children who for the first time in their lives are herded into a classroom and told to obey orders. Some curious warmth that was almost tangible shone out of Miss Honey's face when she spoke to a confused and homesick newcomer to the class.

From Matilda by Roald Dahl

The Grand High Witch

That face of hers was the most frightful and frightening thing I have ever seen. Just looking at it gave me the shakes all over. It was so crumpled and wizened, so shrunken and shrivelled, it looked as though it had been pickled in vinegar. It was a fearsome and ghastly sight. There was something terribly wrong with it, something foul and putrid and decayed. It seemed quite literally to be rotting away at the edges, and in the middle of the face, around the mouth and cheeks. I could see the skin all cankered and worm-eaten, as though maggots were working away in there.

The brilliant snake's eyes that were set so deep in that dreadful rotting worm-eaten face glared unblinkingly at the witches who sat facing her. "You may rree-moof your gloves!" she shouted. Her voice, I noticed, had that same hard metallic quality as the voice of the witch I had met under the conker tree, only it was far louder and much much harsher. It rasped. It grated. It snarled. It scraped. It shrieked. And it growled.

From The Witches by Roald Dahl

People to **Like** *and* **Dislike**

National Literacy Strategy Year 4 Term 1:

Write character sketches focusing on small details to evoke sympathy or dislike.

Read aloud to the class the character descriptions on the photocopiable page. Ask the children to read them again carefully. Talk about each of the characters with the children. Ask them what they have learnt about the character of Miss Honey from the passage. Through the character sketch we learn a great deal about Miss Honey as a person but not about what she looks like. How do the children imagine she looks? Ask them to pick out words and phrases which make the reader like Miss Honey.

Ask the children what they have learnt about the Grand High Witch's looks and character. Ask the children to pick out words and phrases which they feel are most effective at making the reader dislike the witch.

Next ask the children to think of someone they know who they could describe in detail and who would evoke sympathy or dislike. This could be based on a purely fictional character or a real person. Ask the children to jot down ideas for their writing, thinking carefully about what the person looks like, his/her character, habits, and things the person does which makes you like or dislike them.

There is a writing support sheet for those children who have difficulty in thinking up ideas for this.

People to Like *and* Dislike

Name: _____ **Date:** _____

Here are some ideas to help you. Can you think of some more?

Looks

Firstly, make a list of words which describe what he / she looks like. Think about hair, face, clothes etc.

Tidy, neat/ greasy matted hair
smiling/ scowling face
gentle, kind/ rough hurting hands

Character

Now add to these words which tell you about his/ her character.

Mean/ kind
funny/ sad
helpful/ nasty
lots of friends/ lonely
makes people laugh/ cry
cheats/ honest

What They Do

Think about things your character does.
Can you add some more to this list?

Copies your work/ helps you when you are stuck

Cheats at playtime games/ is a good sport/ joins in with others.

Scribbles on your book/ helps you to draw when you are finding it hard to do.

Stamps on people's toes/ helps people who are hurt.

People to Like and Dislike

Name: _____ **Date:** _____

Use the writing frame to gather ideas about the character you have chosen to write about.

Looks/Appearance

Character/ Personality

Habits/ What They Do

Evacuees

From Friend or Foe by Michael Morpurgo

The story, which follows, is set in the Second World War. David and the other school children are being evacuated from London and are about to embark on the journey south to Devon. There they will be placed with families who will look after them until it is safe to return home…

"Right then." Miss Evers folded her piece of paper. "We're all here, and it's time to go. Say goodbye as quick as ever you can. The train leaves Paddington at half past eight, and we have to be there at least an hour before. So hurry it up now – and don't forget your gas masks."

David felt the case being handed to him. "Goodbye, David. And don't worry. It'll be all right. I'll send a letter as soon as I can. God bless." She kissed him quickly on the cheek and turned away. He watched her until she disappeared at the end of the street. All around him there was crying; boys he'd never dreamt could cry, weeping openly, and mothers holding on to each other as they walked away. He was glad his mother hadn't cried, and it helped him to see so many of his friends as miserable as he felt himself. He blinked back the tears that had gathered in his eyes and wiped his face before turning towards the station.

The warmth of the Underground came up to meet them as the school trooped down the silent, unmoving escalator. They followed Miss Evers along the tunnels, down the stairways and out on to the platform. Tucky came alongside David and dropped his suitcase.

"H'lo, Davey."

"H'lo, Tucky." They were old friends and there was nothing more to be said.

They did not have long to wait. There was a distant rumble and then a rush of warm, oily wind that blew their eyes closed as it rushed into the platform. Miss Evers counted them as they pushed and jostled into the carriage, herding them in like sheep, so that every corner of the carriage was filled. The doors clicked and hissed shut, and the train jerked forward, throwing everyone against each other.

David watched the last Highbury and Islington sign as long as he could, craning his neck until the carriage plunged into the darkness of the tunnel and it was gone.

WAR DECLARED OFFICIAL

Evacuees

National Literacy Strategy Year 4 Term 1:

To write independently, linking own experience to situations in historical stories e.g. How would I have responded? What would I do next?

Read the passage 'Evacuees' aloud to the children. Find out what they understand about evacuation during the Second World War. Ask them how they would feel if they too had had to move from the city to the countryside. What would be the differences they would experience moving from a busy city to a village?

Ask them to imagine what it was like to go and live with a family who were strangers to them. What problems might they experience? What might they learn if they went to live in the countryside? Would they miss parents and friends? Would they miss the town or city?

Ask the children to write the story that follows the passage on the photocopiable page, beginning from the point at which the children arrive at the village in Devon and are picked out by the families who are to look after them and are taken to their new home. Write the story in the third person (e.g. He/she was sent to etc.) describing what happened to one of the children.

The children should go on in their story to describe the people and the home to which the child was taken. They should write about the new life the evacuee experienced in which he/she learned about life on a farm and in the countryside. Is the evacuee happy or sad? Does he/she eventually return to the city and is he/she reunited with parents?

There is a Writing Frame to aid planning and a Writing Support Sheet to aid children who struggle with this activity.

Evacuees

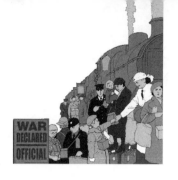

Name: _____ **Date:** _____

The girl's name was called. "Helen Smith! You are to go with Mr and Mrs Thomas," the teacher ordered in a firm voice.

The old couple came over to greet the girl. Mr Thomas said kindly, " _____

_____

_____

_____

They took Helen back to their farm and showed her around. There were _____

_____

_____

Then Mrs Thomas took the girl into the kitchen. She gave her _____

_____

_____

_____

Next Helen was shown to her bedroom which was _____

_____

_____

_____

The following day Mr Thomas said that Helen could help him on the farm. She _____

_____

_____

When the war was over _____

_____

_____

Evacuees

Name: _____ Date:_____

The Story Setting: What was the village like? What was the evacuee's new home like?

Characters: Think about the evacuee and the person or family that he/she went to live with.

The story begins when the train arrives at the village. The evacuees are taken to the village hall where they are chosen by the new families who will care for them. Think about how they feel .

The evacuee is taken to his/her new home. Who takes the child? Are they kind? Do they welcome the evacuee?

What is the home like to which the child is taken? Are there any other children there? Are they given jobs to do?

Is the evacuee happy to stay? Does the child run away or does he/she remain there for the rest of the war? Does he/she return home?

Hansel and Gretel

Once upon a time there were two children named Hansel and Gretel who lived with their father and step-mother, in a cottage at the edge of a wood. One day the step-mother complained to her husband, who was a wood-cutter, that the family was short of food. "Husband dear, we must get rid of Hansel and Gretel for there is little food left. There is only enough for you and me!" The poor wood-cutter was worried and upset but he obeyed his wife and sent the children into the woods to look for fire-wood.

Hansel, who was a bright boy gathered pebbles and put them in his pocket. He knew that it was easy to get lost in the woods and so if the children were to drop pebbles along their way, then they could easily find their way home. That is what they did and much to the wicked step-mother's disgust, the children returned home with a bundle of wood. The next day the wood-cutter again took his children deep into the wood, and asked them, once again to collect wood. This time the children had no pebbles, however they did have a piece of bread. As they walked along through the woods, collecting sticks, they dropped crumbs of bread, so they could find their way home. Unfortunately, birds came along and ate the bread, so the children were well and truly lost in the wood. As they tried to find their way home, they came upon a strange little house, made entirely from ginger-bread, cakes and sweets. The children ate hungrily, until a strange old lady appeared, "Come in dear children! You must be tired and hungry," she said, in a kindly voice. However this old lady was far from kind, she was in fact, a witch! As soon as the children went inside, she grabbed hold of Hansel and put him in a cage. She made Gretel work for her and told Hansel that she planned to fatten him up to eat!

One day, the witch was checking the fire to see if it was hot. Gretel saw her opportunity, and pushed the old witch so hard that she fell right in and was burned up! Then Gretel quickly unlocked the cage and released her brother. In the cottage there was treasure, which the children gathered up and put in their pockets. Then they wandered back through the woods until they found themselves back home. Their father opened the door and was delighted to see them. "Your step-mother has gone!" he announced.

The children showed him the treasures they had found. They were now no longer poor and were never short of food again!`

20

National Literacy Strategy Year 4 Term 1:

To write play scripts e.g. using known stories as a basis.

Read the story aloud to the children. Ask them to choose a part of the story to make into a play script. Model a section of play script on the board. Emphasise the importance of layout and of writing in the present tense. Explain that stage directions should be written in brackets.

The scene should be preceded by a list of characters who appear. Following the character list are details of where the scene takes place.

It would be useful if groups of children were to cover different parts of the story. Each small scene, could then be pieced together to form a complete script of the story of 'Hansel and Gretel'. These could then be acted out.

The children may well need several attempts to produce a script with which they are satisfied.

For children who struggle with this activity or who have special needs, there is a Writing Support Sheet.

Writing Support Sheet

Name: _____ **Date:** _____

Hansel and Gretel are Captured by the Wicked Witch! – A Play Script

Characters

Hansel . . . . .brother of Gretel who is lost in the wood.

Gretel sister of . . . . . ._____.

The Witch . . . . .who lives in the house made of_____.

Setting . . . . _____.

Hansel   Look sister ! What's that over there in the trees?

Gretel   I think it's a house. Let's go and see!

(The two children go to look and find that _____ *)*

Hansel   Look Gretel, the house is made of cake and sweets! I am so hungry. Are you?

Gretel   _____

(The children pull off chunks of _____ *)*

Gretel   Look! There is an old lady over there, perhaps_____

Hansel   Yes you are right, perhaps she will help us to _____

Witch   Hello Children!_____

Gretel   We are lost. Can you _____

Witch   You poor dears! Come with me and _____

(The witch takes them by the hand and leads them towards _____ *)*

Hansel   Thank-you old lady. You are _____

(Suddenly, she grabs the children and takes them inside. She locks _____ *)*

Witch   Ha-Ha… Now you cannot _____

        Hansel I shall eat_____

        Gretel, you will work_____

(Hansel is put in a cage, so he cannot _____ *)*

Colour Poems

What is Red?

Red is a sunset
Blazing and bright.
Red is feeling brave
With all your might.
Red is a sunburn
Spot on your nose.
Sometimes red
Is a red red rose.
Red squiggles out
When you cut your hand.
Red is a brick
And the sound of a band.
Red is hotness
You get inside
When you're embarrassed
And want to hide.
Fire-cracker, fire-engine
Fire-flicker red-
And when you're angry
Red runs through your head.
Red is an Indian,
A Valentine heart,
The trimmings on
A circus cart.
Red is lipstick
Red is a shout
Red is a signal
That says: 'Watch out!'
Red is a great big
Rubber ball.
Red is the giant-est
Colour of all.
Red is a show-off,
No doubt about it –
But can you imagine
Living without it?

Mary O'Neill

Colour Poems

National Literacy Strategy Year 4 Term 1:

To write poems based on personal or imagined experience, linked to poems read. List brief phrases and words, experiment by trimming or extending sentences; experiment with powerful and expressive verbs.

Read aloud the poem 'What is Red?' by Mary O'Neill, to the class. Then read the poem aloud together. Talk about the different aspects of red that the poem describes. Bring out the idea that the poem includes not just objects that are red but talks about feelings such as anger and sounds which remind the poet of red, such as the sound of a band.

Talk about the way the poem is set out with quite short lines, each beginning with a capital letter. Point out examples of careful choice of words, such as 'red is a sunset blazing and bright'.

Ask the children to choose their favourite colour. They should brainstorm as many different things that they associate with it under three headings:

'Objects', 'Sounds' and 'Feelings'.

Use the children's ideas to model a poem on the board. Look at the finished version for ways of improving the language to make the poem as lively and descriptive as possible. Next erase the class poem and ask the children to compose one of their own. The children should be given the opportunity to revise and re-draft their poems, until a final version is achieved.

There is a Writing Support Sheet for those children who lack ideas or who have special needs. The finished poems can be read aloud at a class poetry reading and perhaps be included in a class anthology.

Colour Poems

Name: _____ **Date:** _____

Blue

Objects - paint, woolly jumper, Dad's best tie, a sports car, a blue sky in summer.

Sounds - music of a flute, a trickling stream, the sound of the sea, the wind whistling through the trees, a baby's cry.

Feelings - sadness, the feeling you get when no-one lets you join the game, loneliness. A sad film or song.

White

Objects - a clean handkerchief, freshly fallen snow, a bride, a clean page in your book. a glass of fresh milk.

Sounds - a whisper, a baby's breath, a quiet piece of music, the shrill note of a bird singing.

Feelings - the feeling you get in a church or an empty building, being alone in a silent room, being tired.

Green

Objects - a tall tree, a field of grass, a front door, a felt tip or crayon, a lorry, a shiny leaf, a cubs uniform.

Sounds - a happy tune, a cheerful hello, a joke, the sound of lambs in the field, a whistle.

Feelings - the feeling you get playing your favourite game, when life is going well, the good part of a dream.

The Borrowers

Arrietty lives with her father, Pod and her mother Homily, under the floor-boards of a wealthy house. They are tiny people, no taller than a finger, who had made themselves a comfortable home with the bits and pieces Pod had 'borrowed' from upstairs. Pod would go on expeditions, when he knew the humans were not around, and fill his 'borrowing bag' with items that his family needed. Arrietty had begged to be taken on one of these trips upstairs, and her father finally agreed she should go. To reach upstairs, they had to go through a hole in the floor near the grand-father clock.

As she followed her father down the passage Arrietty's heart began to beat faster. Now the moment had come at last she found it almost too much to bear. She felt light and trembly, and hollow with excitement. They had three borrowing-bags between the two of them, 'In case', Pod had explained, 'we pick up something. (A bad borrower loses many a chance for lack of an extra bag), and Pod laid these down to open the first gate, which was latched by a safety-pin. It was a big pin, too strongly sprung for little hands to open, and Arrietty watched her father swing his whole weight on the bar and his feet kick loose off the ground. Hanging from his hands, he shifted his weight along the pin towards the curved sheath and, as he moved, the pin sprang open and he, in the same instant, jumped free. 'You couldn't do that,' he remarked, dusting his hands, 'too light. Nor could your mother. Come along now. Quietly….'

There were other gates; all of which Pod left open 'Never shut a gate on the way out,' he explained in a whisper, 'you might need to get back quick.' and, after a while, Arrietty saw a faint light at the end of the passage. She pulled her father's sleeve. 'Is that it?' she whispered.

Pod stood still. 'Quietly, now,' he warned her. 'Yes, that's it: the hole under the clock!' As he said these words, Arrietty felt breathless but, outwardly, she made no sign. 'There are three steps up to it,' Pod went on, 'steep like, so mind how you go. When you're under the clock you just stay there; don't let your mind wander and keep your eyes on me. If all's clear, I'll give you the sign.'

The steps were high and a little uneven but Arrietty took them more lightly than Pod. As she scrambled past the jagged edges of the hole she had a sudden blinding glimpse of molten gold: it was spring sunshine on the pale stones of the hall floor.

From The Borrowers by Mary Norton

The Borrowers

National Literacy Strategy Year 4 Term 1:

To use paragraphs in story writing to organise and sequence the narrative.

Read the story aloud to the class and then ask the children to re-read it by themselves. Ask the children what they imagine Homily, Pod, and Arrietty to look like. What is their home under the floorboards like? Can the children think of everyday objects that Pod might have borrowed to use in their home? For example, they might use handkerchiefs as bed covers or a thimble as a washing up bowl, or several match boxes piled on top of one another as a set of drawers. Then, talk about who the children imagine lives above the floorboards. Is it a family? Is the story perhaps set in the past when people had servants?

Ask the children to imagine that their story begins from the point at which Arrietty and Pod go through the hole in the floor into the world of the house above the floorboards. What do they imagine the house looks like? (Don't forget they are only very small and everything in the house will seem huge!) What things do Arrietty and Pod see that they decide to put in their 'borrowing bags'? Whilst they are busy looking for items to borrow they may see some of the people from the house. Do Pod and Arrietty remain safely hidden, or are they spotted by the people from upstairs? What finally makes them return home to below the floorboards? Do they manage to take their 'borrowing bags' safely back with them or are they spotted?

There is a Writing Frame for the children to use at the planning stage and for those children who struggle with this activity there is a Writing Support Sheet. When the children have planned their writing they should write their story in full, using their completed Writing Frame as a guide to produce a story in four paragraphs.

The Borrowers

Writing Support Sheet

Name: _____   **Date:** _____

Arrietty and Pod Visit the World of the House Upstairs

Paragraph 1

Arrietty followed Pod, as he climbed carefully through the hole near the grandfather clock. Looking around he saw _____

_____

Everything seemed enormous to Pod and Arrietty, especially _____

_____

Paragraph 2

They looked around for things to borrow. Arrietty saw a piece of string which her mother could use _____

_____

Then Pod spotted some cotton wool. He knew that it would be useful for _____

_____

They spotted a scrap of bright red cloth which could be used_____

_____

Lastly _____

Paragraph 3

As they put their borrowings into a bag, they heard some footsteps. It was _____

_____

They hid _____

They watched as _____ went _____

Next they saw _____

Paragraph 4

Their 'borrowing bags' were well filled. They began to make their way back to the grandfather clock. Suddenly, they heard _____

_____

They quickly hid _____

When it was safe, they decided to _____

_____

Lastly _____

_____

28

The Borrowers

Writing Frame

Name: _____ **Date:** _____

The Story Setting: What was the wealthy house like? What was Arrietty, Homily and Pod's home like?

Characters: Think about how you imagine Pod, Arrietty and Homily look. Also think about who they might see upstairs on their borrowing expeditions.

The story begins at the point at which Arrietty and Pod go through the hole in the floor into the world of upstairs. Describe the house through their eyes.

What things do they decide to 'borrow'? What uses will these things have when they return home?

Which people from upstairs do they see? Do they remain unspotted by them?

What makes them decide to return home to below the floorboards? Do they manage to get their 'borrowing bags' back below stairs? Are they spotted or do they return home safely?

The Chocolate Factory

Charlie has won a golden ticket which gains him entry into Mr Willy Wonka's Chocolate Factory. Charlie is taken to see the Chocolate room....

Mr Wonka opened the door. Five children and nine grown-ups pushed their way in – and oh, what an amazing sight it was that now met their eyes!

They were looking down upon a lovely valley. There were green meadows on either side of the valley, and along the bottom of it there flowed a great brown river.
What is more, there was a tremendous waterfall halfway along the river - a steep cliff over which the water curled and rolled in a solid sheet, and then went crashing down into a boiling churning whirlpool of froth and spray.

Below the waterfall (and this was the most astonishing sight of all), a whole mass of enormous glass pipes were dangling down into the river carrying it away to goodness knows where. And because they were made of glass, you could see the liquid flowing and bubbling along inside them and above the noise of the waterfall, you could hear the never-ending suck-suck-sucking sound of the pipes as they did their work.
Graceful trees and bushes were growing along the riverbanks – weeping willows and alders and tall clumps of rhododendrons with their pink and red and mauve blossoms. In the meadows there were thousands of buttercups.

'There!' cried Mr Wonka, dancing up and down and pointing his gold-topped cane at the great brown river, 'It's all chocolate! Every drop of that river is hot melted chocolate of the finest quality. The very finest quality. There's enough chocolate in there to fill every bathtub in the entire country! And all the swimming pools as well! Isn't it terrific?'

From Charlie and the Chocolate Factory by Roald Dahl

Teacher's Notes

National Literacy Strategy Year 4 Term 2:

To develop use of settings in own writing, making use of work on adjectives and figurative language to describe settings effectively.

Read aloud the description of The Chocolate Room to the children, at least twice. Ask them to go through the passage and highlight words and phrases which they feel are particularly effective. Discuss what makes a good description. Talk about the importance of using adjectives. Again, ask the children to pick out adjectives, which they feel add to the description. Collect together effective verbs in the passage and ask the children to try to say why they like them.

Bring out the point that good description, has to paint a picture in your mind, therefore lots of detail is needed. Emphasise the importance of appealing to more than just the sense of sight. Pick out the sounds that Dahl has included in the passage. Ask the children what smells they might have found in the room.

Then ask the children what they think Mr. Wonka's Inventing Room might have been like. What might he be inventing there? What machinery would be in the room? Who works in the room? What do they look like and what are they wearing? What smells and sounds would be found in the room? Ask the children to draw a picture of how they imagine the Inventing Room to look, in the box on the Writing Frame sheet. When they have done this, they should then go on to think of words and phrases which contain exciting verbs and adjectives to add to the other box on the Writing Frame sheet.

When the children have collected together their ideas they can then begin to write their description. There is a Writing Support Sheet for those children who struggle with this activity.

The Chocolate Factory

Name: _____ **Date:** _____

The Inventing Room was enormous! It was as big as _____

_____

and the roof was as high as _____

Here, Willy Wonka was inventing _____

_____

and _____ . Huge machines made of _____

went all the way down the middle of the brightly painted Inventing Room. All around, there

were busy little workers who _____

_____

They looked _____

_____

Into the great machines they poured _____

_____

to make _____

At the far end of the great machine, out came _____

_____

and _____

_____

The sounds that could be heard in the room were of _____

_____

The sound was _____

The smell that filled the room was of _____

_____

It was wonderful, just like _____

_____

At one side of the room, workers were busy _____

_____

The room was amazing ! Charlie had never _____

_____

The Chocolate Factory

Name: _____ **Date:** _____

In this box draw a picture of how you imagine the Inventing Room in Willy Wonka's Factory might have looked. Try to add lots of detail to your picture.

In this box, gather together words and ideas you can use in your description of the Inventing Room. Remember to add as many adjectives to nouns as possible to try to paint a picture of the room in the reader's imagination.

Hands

Hands
Stroking
Comforting and caring
Giving and sharing
Hands
Cleaning and cooking
Mending and making
Hands
Dancing
Painting and moulding
Sewing and writing
Hands

Hands
Grabbing
Snatching and tearing
Hands
Squeezing and pinching
Breaking and bending
Hands
Stealing
Hitting and hurting
Scratching and clawing
Hands

Hands

National Literacy Strategy Year 4 Term 2:

To write poetry based on the structure and style of poems read.

Read the poem aloud to the children and then ask them to read it aloud as a group. Talk about the kind of hands described in each verse of the poem. Ask the children to think about other examples of good and bad hands, which could have been included in either of the verses. Collect these ideas together on the board under the headings 'Good Hands' and 'Unkind Hands'.

Next, question the children about the structure of the poem. Bring out the idea that after each couple of lines, the word 'Hands' stands alone on a new line. Bring out the point that it is unnecessary for the lines to rhyme, and to note that each line is quite short.

When the children have collected their ideas, they can begin to formulate them into a poem modelled on the photocopiable one. The children may want to draft these several times until they are satisfied with the finished poem. These can then be read aloud at a class poetry reading and could be put into a class anthology.

For those children who struggle to come up with ideas there is a Writing Support Sheet.

Hands

Name: _____ **Date:** _____

Good Things Hands Can Do
Collect words and ideas for your own poem about hands. These will be used for the first verse of your poem.

> Think about hobbies that people have. Here are some ideas. Can you think of some more?
> Stitching, making, carving, drawing...

> Now, think of some helpful actions that people could do with their hands. Here are some ideas. Can you think of some more?
> Dusting, scrubbing, decorating, baking, building...

> Think of some kind actions that people make with their hands. Here are some ideas. Can you think of some more?
> Loving, sharing, holding, helping, warming...

Unkind Things Hands Can Do
Now collect ideas for the second verse of your poem, which is about the unkind things that hands can do.

> Think about the playground and the times that people use their hands in nasty ways. Here are some ideas to help you. Can you think of some more of your own?
> Pushing, poking, pulling, ripping...

> Can you think of some wrong actions that hands are used for? Here are some ideas. Can you think of some more?
> Taking, smashing, wrecking, spoiling, robbing, fighting...

The Isle of Rundersmere

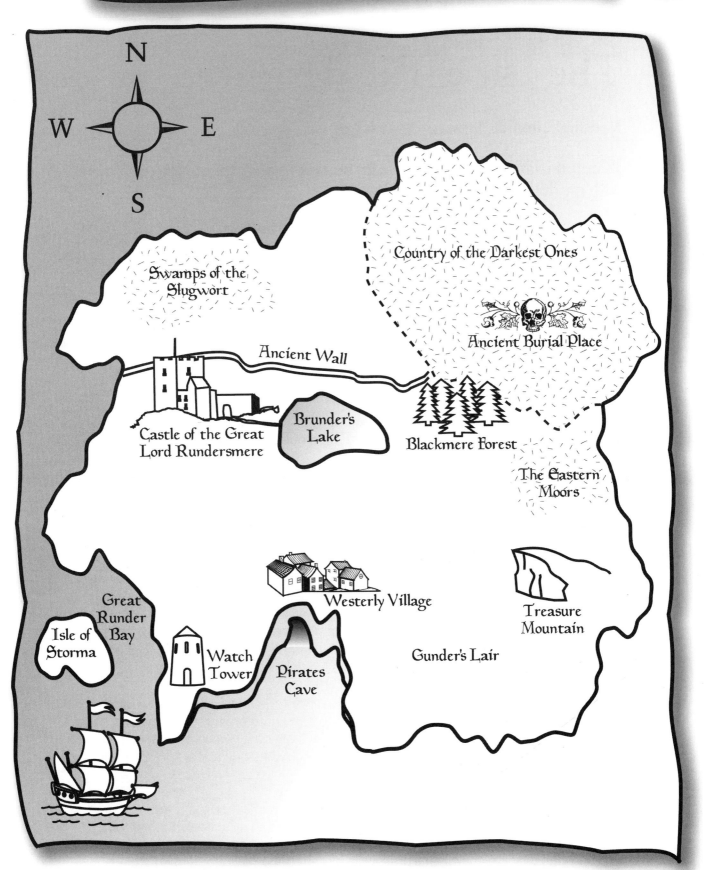

Swamps of the Slugwort

Country of the Darkest Ones

Ancient Burial Place

Ancient Wall

Castle of the Great Lord Rundersmere

Brunder's Lake

Blackmere Forest

The Eastern Moors

Westerly Village

Treasure Mountain

Great Runder Bay

Isle of Storma

Watch Tower

Pirates Cave

Gunder's Lair

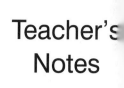

The Isle of Rundersmere

National Literacy Strategy Year 4 Term 2:

To collaborate with others to write stories in chapters, using plans with particular audiences in mind.

The children should each be given a copy of the map 'The Isle of Rundersmere'. The children should be given time to look carefully at the map. Talk about its different features together so that the class understands terms and can begin to build up an imaginary picture of the Island.

Explain to the children that they are going to write a story in chapters working in a group of three. The story will have three chapters and each member of the group will be responsible for writing one of these. When the story is complete the group will be able to take their story to another class, perhaps Year 2, and read it aloud to the children. The story might also be read by individuals in reading time.

Explain to the children that the chapter headings will be as follows. These should be displayed clearly in the classroom, for group reference.

Chapter 1   Landing on the Isle of Rundersmere

Chapter 2   Exploring the Island

Chapter 3   Treasure!

The children should then be divided into groups of three members. Explain to the children that before writing they must agree on a number of issues. It is important that the characters remain the same throughout the story and that they agree on how they got to the island in the first place. They should then agree on the special treasure that can be found there. It would be useful to agree on enemies or problems they might face on the island. Looking at the map will help the children to generate ideas.

Finally, they must decide on whether they are successful in finding the treasure and how the story is resolved. Do they remain on the island or return home again? There is a Group-Planning Sheet to help the children clarify their ideas. It is important that they each have a copy of this to make sure their chapter remains true to the agreed group plan.

To aid the children in the writing of their own particular chapter there is a writing frame. When the stories are complete, the group should look carefully at each chapter to ensure they link together and have no glaring errors of character or story line. The stories, when they are in their final draft, will be ready to be read aloud to an audience.

The Isle of Rundersmere

Before you begin writing, you will have to agree as a group on a number of points. Use this chart to help you.

Characters

Decide on two or three main characters who will appear in each chapter of your story. Think about names, what each character looks like, how old he/she is, and the kind of person he/she is (funny, serious, adventurous, brave).

Character 1

Character 2

Character 3

Agree together, how these characters got to the Isle of Rundersmere. Note down your ideas.

What treasure might they search for on the island?

What problems or enemies might they face on the island? Do they make any friends or meet people who will help them? Use the map to help you think of ideas.

Are they successful in finding the treasure? How is the story resolved? Do they stay on the island or do they return home?

The Isle of Rundersmere

Writing Frame

Name: _____ **Date:** _____

Chapter Title:

The Story Setting:

Characters in this chapter:

This chapter begins with:

The main part of the chapter is about:

The chapter ends when:

The First Time

School

Laurie Lee describes his first day at school….

I arrived at the school just three feet tall and fatly wrapped in my scarves. The playground roared like a rodeo, and the potato burned through my thigh. Old boots, ragged stockings, torn trousers and skirts, went skating and skidding around me. The rabble closed in; I was encircled; grit flew in my face like shrapnel. Tall girls with frizzled hair, and huge boys with sharp elbows, began to prod me with hideous interest. They plucked at my scarves, spun me round like a top, screwed my nose, and stole my potato.

From: 'Cider with Rosie' by Laurie Lee.

In this passage, Orion the cat, shows Plop the baby Barn Owl the beauty of the night. He persuades Plop to make his first night flight and not to be afraid of the dark

'I love moonlight,' said the cat. 'Moonlight is magic. It turns everything it touches to silver, especially on frosty nights like this. Oh, come with me, Plop, and I will show you a beautiful world of sparkling silver - the secret night time world of cats and owls. The daytime people are asleep. It is all ours, Plop. Will you come?'…..

They sat together on the highest roof and looked down over the sleeping town, a black velvet cat and a little white powder puff of owl. 'Well?' said the cat.
'It is – it is – oh, I haven't the words for it,' breathed Plop. 'But you are right, Orion. I am a night bird after all. Fancy sleeping all night and missing this!'
'And this is only one sort of night,' said Orion. 'There are lots of other kinds, all beautiful. There are hot, scented summer nights; and cold windy nights when the scuffling clouds make ragged shadows across the ground; and breathless, thundery nights which are suddenly slashed with jagged white lightning; and fresh spring nights when even the day birds can't bear to sleep....

From: 'The Owl Who Was Afraid of the Dark' by Jill Tomlinson

The First Time

National Literacy Strategy Year 4 Term 2:

To write own examples of descriptive, expressive language based on those read. Link to work on adjectives and similes.

Read aloud, at least twice, the passages on the photocopiable page. Ask the children which part of each description they liked most and why.

Next, ask the children to go through and highlight the words and phrases that they find most effective. Talk about the way that adding adjectives, similes and metaphors in writing makes the description much more exciting for the reader. Explain that it is like painting in the details on a picture with words. Pick out particularly effective examples of expressive language and talk about them with the children - for example:
"The playground roared like a rodeo."
"Grit flew in my face like shrapnel."
"They sat together... a black velvet cat and a little white powder puff of owl."
"There are hot, scented summer nights when the scuffling clouds make ragged shadows across the ground."

Talk about the first time the children went swimming/to cubs/to brownies/ to a new school/to the dentist or to a fairground. Ask the children to make notes on the details they remember with as many descriptive words and phrases added as possible.

The children should then form these into a short descriptive piece of writing entitled 'The First Time'. Allow the children time to draft these, where time allows, until they feel they have achieved the best piece of descriptive writing that they can.

There is a writing support sheet for those children who struggle with this activity.

The First Time

Name: _____   Date: _____

My First Visit to the Dentist
Waiting, quiet people sitting still. Dentist – towering over you, goggles, moaning sound of the drill and clanking of dentist's tools. Sharp smell of antiseptic. Peering at dentist's face.

My First Day at School
Children's voices, laughing, crying, screaming, shouting, wanting their Mums. Huge classroom, tall teacher, hard wooden chairs and brightly coloured plastic tables. Smell of school dinners. Children dashing, running, shouting, playing in the playground.

My First Visit to the Fairground
Lights dazzling, flashing on and off, colours red, blue, green yellow like fireworks on Bonfire night. Sounds – sirens, screams, laughing voices. Smells – sizzling hot dogs, onions, pink fluffy candy floss, fumes of rides like car fumes.

My First Swimming Lesson
The hugeness of the swimming pool, echo of children shouting, laughing, splashing in the water, sound of crashing as someone dives in, strong smell of chlorine fills the air, feeling shivery and cold as you wait to get in, the icy moment when you get into the water.

Making Notes

Susan wrote to her friend Emma to tell her about her school day. Here is what she wrote down.

My School Day

We set off for school at half past eight, so that we will get there for nine o'clock when school begins. After registering, we go to assembly in the school hall. It generally lasts for about half an hour. Then it is time for the Numeracy Hour. After that we go out to play at about half past ten. At eleven o'clock the bell rings. We line up then we go back into class. It is time for the Literacy Hour. At twelve o'clock we go into the hall for dinner. When we have finished, we go out in the playground, unless it is raining, then we stay in our classroom. We have two lessons on a Monday afternoon. Firstly it is Science until half past two, and then it is History until half-past three when we go home.

Emma's teacher asked her to find out about life at a different school, so she made notes on Susan's day from her letter. This is what she wrote down:

Notes on Susan's Day at Hill Top Primary School

9.00	School begins
9.00 - 9.30	Assembly in the school hall
9.30 - 10.30	Numeracy Hour
10.30 - 11.00	Playtime
11.00 - 12.00	Literacy hour
12.00 - 1.00	Dinner time – when finished eating go outside to play or if wet stay in the classroom
1.00 - 2.30	Science
2.30 - 3.30	History
3.30	Home time

Making Notes

National Literacy Strategy Year 4 Term 2:

To edit down a sentence or passage, by deleting the less important elements, e.g. repetitions, asides, secondary considerations and discuss the reasons for editorial choices.

Read the information that Susan wrote to Emma concerning her school day at Hill Top Primary School, found on the photocopiable page. Talk about this with the children and then explain that Emma used the information to make notes on Susan's day.

Read the notes aloud to the children. Talk to the children about what is meant by making notes. Discuss the details which are included and why some things are left out. Talk about the idea that notes need not be in full sentences and that words can be left out. Talk about how setting it out clearly is very important so that it can be read quickly and clearly, with the most important points standing out.

Next, read aloud together the passage about the zoo keeper's day. Discuss with the children the events of his day, so the passage is fully understood. Ask them to think about and look again at the notes made on Susan's day at Hill Top Primary School. Ask the children to imagine that they have been asked to make notes on the zoo keeper's day, for a new zoo keeper's helper who is to start work soon at the zoo.

The information should be shortened and set out like Susan's notes. For those children who struggle with this activity it would be useful to begin to model the note making on the board together. The children could finish this themselves once they have a clearer understanding of what is expected.

Making Notes

Name: _____ **Date:** _____

Read the passage about a zoo-keeper's day. Then make notes in the box for a new zoo keeper's helper, so he knows what to do.

My Job as a Zoo Keeper

I generally arrive at the zoo at 8 o'clock. First of all I go into the zoo kitchen and prepare the food for the animals. This takes about an hour. At nine o'clock I feed the animals in this order – firstly the monkeys, followed by the elephants, then the lions and last of all the giraffes. The animals get used to me feeding them like this and they wait for me. It takes about an hour from first to last. At 10 o'clock I go and check on the new baby chimpanzees and play with them, so they get used to being handled. At half past ten, I go for my tea break. At about eleven o'clock the vet comes and does his rounds, checking the animals are fine and healthy. This can take about an hour and a half. At half past twelve I go for my dinner. The afternoon from 1.30 till 3.00 is spent cleaning out the cages. Then I spend until four o'clock in the kitchen preparing the animals evening feed. Again it takes an hour then another hour to feed them. I go home at five o'clock.

Going Fishing

One day…. Some children came to our house and asked my mother if I could go fishing with them. They had jam jars with string on them, and fishing nets and sandwiches and lemonade. My mother said "Yes" – I could go with them; and she found me a jam jar and a fishing net, and cut me some sandwiches.

Then my naughty little sister said, "I want to go! I want to go!" Just like that. So my mother said I might as well take her too.

Then my mother cut some sandwiches for my little sister, but she didn't give her a jam jar or a fishing net because she said she was too little to go near the water. My mother gave my little sister a basket to put stones in, because my little sister liked to pick up stones, and she gave me a big bottle of lemonade to carry for both of us.

My mother said, "You mustn't let your little sister get herself wet. You must keep her away from the water." And I said, "All right, Mother, I promise."

So we went off to the little river, and we took our shoes off and our socks off, and tucked up our clothes, and we went into the water to catch fish with our fishing nets and we filled our jam jars with water to put the fishes in when we caught them. And we said to my naughty little sister, "You mustn't come, you'll get yourself wet."

Well, we paddled and paddled and fished and fished, but we didn't catch any fish at all; not even one tiny little one. Then a boy said, "Look, there is your little sister in the water too!"

And, do you know, my naughty little sister had walked right into the water with her shoes and socks on, and she was trying to fish with her basket. I said, "Get out of the water," and she said, "No."

From 'My Naughty Little Sister' by Dorothy Edwards

Going Fishing

National Literacy Strategy Year 4 Term 3:

To explore the main issues of a story by writing a story about a dilemma and the issues it raises for the character.

Read the passage from 'My Naughty Little Sister' aloud to the children. Ask them what they think will happen next in the story. Talk about what you should do if someone gets into difficulty in water. Explain that it would be foolish to go in after the person in case you too got into difficulties. Explain that it would be sensible first to get help from a nearby adult. If there was no one near, then you could look for a strong branch for the person in difficulties to grab hold of.

Ask the children to write the story from the point at which the photocopiable passage ends. The children should use the writing frame provided to plan their story and then they should write the story using their plan to help them.

For those children who have special needs or who struggle to think up ideas of their own there is a partly completed story for them to add to.

When the stories are completed it would be interesting to read some of them aloud or to add them to a class anthology of children's writing.

Going Fishing

Name: _____ Date: _____

Get out of the water now!" I shouted to my sister. "Mum will _____
_____ ".

watched, but my little sister just _____
_____

'No, I won't come out," she shouted, in a loud voice. "I'm going to _____
_____ and you can't stop me!"

She began to wade out into the deeper water. I saw her _____
_____

All of a sudden, I heard her shout, "Help I'm slipping!" Then she _____
_____

I knew it was silly to go out into the deep water _____
_____

I grabbed a strong branch lying on the bank. I _____
_____

My sister grasped the branch and _____
_____

My friends quickly ran up the bank and shouted for help. Soon _____
_____

A lady and man ran to the edge of the water. They shouted, "Don't worry we'll ____ ".
I pulled my sister to the water's edge. She was _____
_____

The lady helped me to _____
_____

The lady's husband rang my mother to _____
_____

Soon my mother arrived looking upset and cross. She said, "Are you alright? _____
_____ ".

"Why did you let your sister go in the water? You should have _____
_____ ".

I explained that _____
My mother was not cross for long. However she said to my naughty little sister in a very stern
voice, "Next time I let you go out with your sister you must _____
_____ ".

Going Fishing

Name: _____ **Date:** _____

The Story Setting: What was the little river like?

Characters: Think about what you imagine the naughty little sister and her older brother or sister to be like.

The story begins at the point at which the photocopiable passage ends when the little sister disobeys her mother's orders. What does she do? How does her brother or sister react?

What happens next? Does she continue to disobey? Does she get into danger?

What does the older brother or sister do?

What happens at the end of the story? What happens when the children's mother comes on the scene?

Goldilocks
and the Three Bears

Once upon a time there were three bears that lived together, in a cottage in the woods. One day Mother Bear made some porridge for breakfast, but as it was too hot, Father Bear said, "Come on, let's go for a walk in the woods whilst this porridge is cooling!"
So, together with Baby Bear they went off for a walk.

Meanwhile, a little girl called Goldilocks was also out in the woods for a walk. She was passing the house of the three bears when she noticed that the door was open, so she went inside to explore. There was no one there, so Goldilocks went into the kitchen

where she saw three bowls of porridge. She felt hungry, so she tried the first bowl which was the biggest. It was too hot! She then tried the medium- sized bowl, but it was too salty! Lastly she tried the tiny bowl. It tasted just right! Soon, she had eaten it all up.

Next, she saw three chairs. She sat on the big chair but it was too high! She tried the medium-sized chair but it was too hard. Finally, she tried the tiny little chair and that was just right! But, oh dear, Goldilocks was too heavy for the little chair and it broke under her weight.

Well, Goldilocks decided to look in the bedroom. There she found three beds belonging to the three bears. She was beginning to feel rather tired so she climbed onto the big bed but it was too hard! Next, she climbed onto the medium – sized bed, but that was too soft. Finally, Goldilocks, lay down on the tiny little bed. She felt so comfortable that in no time at all she fell soundly asleep.

The three bears, meanwhile had returned to have their breakfast. When they went into the kitchen they could see that someone had been eating their porridge. Baby bear began to cry when he saw that someone had eaten up all of his porridge.

Then the three bears noticed that someone had been sitting on their chairs and that poor Baby Bear's chair was broken!

The three bears were about to go into the bedroom when Goldilocks heard them coming! She woke up and, as quick as a flash she jumped out of bed and ran out of the house as quickly as she could.

"There she is, the naughty little girl who has eaten my porridge, broken my chair and has been sleeping in my bed!" Baby Bear shouted.
It was too late. Goldilocks had gone!

National Literacy Strategy Year 4 Term 3:

To write an alternative ending for a known story and to discuss how this would change the reader's view of the characters and events of the original story.

Read the photocopiable story of the Three Bears aloud to the children. Talk about the story. Ask the children if they can remember reading it when they were younger. Ask them how they imagine the three bears to be. Were they kindly or fierce? Bring out the way that the original story makes them seem fierce as Goldilocks runs away when she hears them coming.

Ask the children to think about what might have happened in the story if the bears had met Goldilocks and not been cross about the things that she had done. What might have happened, once Goldilocks realised that they had forgiven her and wanted to be friends?

Ask the children to rewrite the end of the story from the point at which they find Goldilocks fast asleep in bed. They should write about Goldilocks' shock and horror as she realises that she has been caught. However she soon realises that the three bears are not as nasty as she thinks they are but are really kindly. The story should go on to say what happens next - perhaps they all become friends. Baby Bear and Goldilocks might even play together.

There is a Writing Frame to aid the children in their planning of the story and a Writing Support Sheet for those children who struggle with this activity or who have special needs. When the children have finished writing it would be useful for volunteers to read their story aloud.

Talk to the class about the ways in which the new endings they have written change the reader's view of the characters and events of the original story.

Goldilocks and the Three Bears

Name: _____ Date:_____

The three bears returned from their walk. They saw that someone had _____

_____

Next they looked at their chairs. They saw that _____

_____

So they went into the bedroom. There they found _____

_____

Goldilocks was fast asleep so they woke her up and said, " _____

_____

At first Goldilocks was afraid but soon she saw that Father Bear was laughing!
She said to the bears, " _____
_____ "

Mother Bear replied in a kindly voice, " _____
_____ "

Baby Bear smiled too and said to Goldilocks, " _____
_____ "

They took Goldilocks into the kitchen. Mother Bear made _____

_____

They sat at the table to eat. Goldilocks told them _____

_____

Soon, Goldilocks and Baby Bear were firm friends. They went outside to _____

_____

They had such fun playing _____

_____

Goldilocks looked at her watch. "Oh no, I must go home or _____

_____

However, she asked Baby Bear's parents if it was alright if he could come _____

_____

They said, " _____

_____

The Three Bears walked with Goldilocks to the gate of the cottage. "Come _____
_____ ," Baby Bear shouted.

"You really are _____

"See you next week at my _____ ,"

she shouted back, waving to her new friends as she went.

Writing Frame

Name: _____   **Date:** _____

The Story Setting: What was the cottage like?

Characters: How do you imagine Goldilocks to look? Think about the three bears. Remember they are friendly.

The story begins at the point at which the three bears return to the house. Remember they find Goldilocks!

What happens next when Goldilocks realises that they are not cross with her?

What happens at the end of the story? Do Goldilocks and the three bears meet again, do they become friends?

Smugglers

'A Smuggler's Song' by Rudyard Kipling

If you wake at midnight, and hear a horse's feet
Don't go drawing back the blind, or looking in the street.
Them that asks no questions isn't told a lie.
Watch the wall, my darling, while the Gentlemen go by!
      Five and twenty ponies trotting through the dark-
      Brandy for the Parson, 'baccy for the Clerk;
      Laces for a lady, letters for a spy,
      And watch the wall, my darling while the Gentlemen go by!

Running round the woodlump if you chance to find
Little barrels, roped and tarred, all full of brandy-wine,
Don't you shout to come and look, nor use 'em for your play.
Put the brushwood back again- and they'll be gone next day!

If you see a stable-door setting open wide;
If you see a tired horse lying down inside;
If your mother mends a coat cut about and tore;
If the lining's wet and warm- don't you ask no more!

If you meet King George's men, dressed in blue and red,
You be careful what you say, and mindful what is said.
If they call you "pretty maid", and chuck you 'neath the chin,
Don't you tell where no one is, nor yet where no one's been!

Knocks and footsteps round the house - whistles after dark-
You've no call for running out till the house - dogs bark.
Trusty's here, and Pincher's here, and see how dumb they lie-
They don't fret to follow when the Gentlemen go by!

If you do as you've been told, 'likely there's a chance,
You'll be given a dainty doll, all the way from France,
With a cap of Valenciennes, and a velvet hood-
      A present from the Gentlemen, along o'being
        good!
        Five and twenty ponies,
          Trotting through the dark-
          Brandy for the Parson,
          'Baccy for the clerk.
          Them that asks no questions isn't told
           a lie-
            Watch the wall, my darling, while
             the Gentlemen go by!

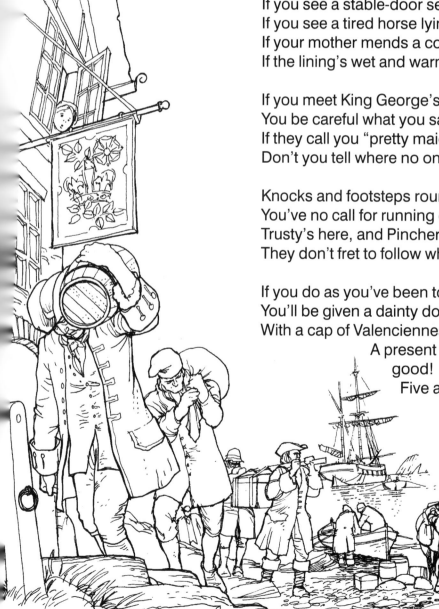

Smugglers

National Literacy Strategy Year 4 Term 3:

To write own longer stories in chapters from story plans.

Read aloud 'A Smuggler's Song' by Rudyard Kipling, at least twice. Look at the poem verse by verse and talk about why smuggling was common in the past, who the 'Gentlemen' and 'King George's men' were. Go on to talk about how people in the village helped the smugglers and the sort of items that might have been smuggled and the reasons for this. The poem is full of mystery and secrecy. Ask the children to choose words and phrases, from the poem which create this atmosphere.

Ask the children to think about ideas for writing a long story in chapters around the theme of smugglers. Ask the children to imagine that they live in a village which is helping the smugglers. Talk about the setting of the story being somewhere like a Cornish or a North Yorkshire village. It would be useful to have posters or pictures of this type of landscape to help fire the children's imaginations and to help them gather words and ideas for the setting. Some children will have endless ideas and be able to plan their chapters with very little support. However, others will find this idea of structuring their work very difficult. There is a Writing Support Sheet and a Writing Frame for those children.

When the children have finished their story plans, they should write their story in full. These could be drafted if time allows. A front and back cover could be designed, after looking at a variety of similar front cover and back cover blurb designs. The finished books could be shared with other younger children or be displayed in the classroom.

 # Smugglers

Name: _____ Date: _____

Here are some words and ideas to help you. Can you think of some more?

The Story Setting: A village in Cornwall, close to the sea, rocky cliffs, caves, deep dark passages, winding streets, small stone cottages, boats, fishermen.

Characters:

Main Character - a girl/boy about eight or nine years old, good at keeping secrets, helps hide the smuggled goods.

His/Her Father - a shop-keeper who wants the wine, lace and brandy to sell in his shop. Jolly, brave, careful, clever at hiding the smuggled goods.

Father's Friend - a landlord of the village inn, 'The Ram's Head', who wants the wine and brandy to sell to his customers.

King George's Men – the soldiers dressed in blue and red uniforms who want to catch the smugglers. Carry swords, and come when no one is expecting them.

French Sailors - strong, brave, cunning and clever, wealthy, able to guide the boat in the dark away from the rocks, dressed like pirates.

Smugglers

Name: _____ **Date:** _____

Chapter 1 Title: The Smugglers are Coming!

Think about who you are in the story.

_____

You are waiting for the smugglers. How do they get there – by boat, at night/ during the day.

_____

Describe how it feels keeping watch. Who is with you? What is the weather like?

_____

The smugglers are seen on the horizon. What signals are used to communicate with them as they get nearer?

_____

Do they finally land? Do they have any problems in doing this?

_____

_____

Chapter 2   Title: The Smugglers Have Landed!

Where do the smugglers land the boat?

_____

How many come ashore?

_____

How do you help? Do you help to hide the smuggled goods? Where do you hide them - in a cave, an old barn ?

_____

What are the smuggled goods? How many gold coins are given to the smugglers in exchange?

_____

Do the smugglers return straight away to France or do they stay on in the village?

_____

_____

Chapter 3 Title: Disaster Strikes- a Visit by King George's Men!

The goods are hidden but disaster strikes when soldiers come without notice. What happens when they arrive? Where do they search?

_____

What happens during the search? Are you able to distract them from the real hiding place?

_____

How does the story end? Do you succeed in keeping the goods hidden?

_____

_____

Poetry Writing

Evening

Evening
The sound of babies crying

Evening
Wind whistling, rustling in tall trees

Evening
Car doors banging, engines humming

Evening
Voices laughing, people chatting

Evening
Footsteps echoing, people passing

Evening
Cats howling and dogs barking

Evening
Dishes rattling and kettle singing

Evening
Wrapping round me, the warm soft blanket of night.

By Heather Bell

Teacher' Notes

National Literacy Strategy Year 4 Term 3:

To write poems experimenting with different styles and structures, discuss if and why different forms are more suitable than others.

Read aloud the poem 'Evening' at least twice. Talk about the images that are created in the poem. Discuss the particular evening sounds that are described in the poem. What various sounds can be heard in the poem? Why is the poem set out in the way that it is? Does this add to the effectiveness of the poem?

When the children have read and understood the poem, ask them to think of the sounds that you might hear whilst lying in bed at night-time. Gather these together to use later when writing your own poem. Ask the children to write either a poem entitled 'Morning', or one with the title 'Night'. Ask the children to model their poem on the style of the sample poem. There is a Writing Support Sheet for those children who struggle with this activity.

Encourage the children to redraft their poems until they achieve a final version, which attempts to use the best words that they can. The finished poems could be read aloud at a poetry reading session and then be displayed in a class anthology to share with others.

Poetry Writing

Name: _____ **Date:** _____

Here are some ideas to help you write your poem. Can you think of some more of your own?

Morning	**Night**
My brother/sister shrieking	Cats howling
Milk bottles clanking	Cars humming
Crispy bacon sizzling	Babies crying
Mum's voice shouting	The wind whistling
The radio singing	Curtains flapping
The kettle whistling	Footsteps passing

© **Topical Resources.** May be photocopied for classroom use only.

Acrostic Poems
Grandfather Clock

Grey-faced, I stare along the hallway,

Rigid, with a narrow door to my innards.

A wobbly brass catch opens me up.

Not many know how to turn it. Inside my

Darkness hangs a metal pendulum,

Forever swinging from side to side.

A weighted chain, looped round cogs, makes me

Tick, notch after notch. Someone must

Heave the chain to raise that weight

Every twenty-four hours, without fail.

Remember to wind me, before time runs out.

Crafted two hundred years ago yet

Look how sturdily I stand,

Older than any living person.

Crotchety, but as accurate as the sun.

Know this: I am the heartbeat of the house.

From 'Rhyme and Reason' Written by Sylvia Turner

Acrostic Poems
Grandfather Clock

National Literacy Strategy Year 4 Term 3:

To write poems experimenting with different styles and structures….
To produce polished poetry through revision e.g. deleting words, adding words, changing words, reorganising words and lines, experimenting with figurative language.

Read aloud the acrostic poem 'Grandfather Clock' to the children at least twice. Talk about how an acrostic poem is set out. Draw out from the children the way in which 'Grandfather Clock' is written so that the reader imagines that it is actually the clock which is speaking. Ask the children to pick out words and phrases, which they feel, are examples of good description and are well chosen by the poet.

Choose a topic for an acrostic poem, such as 'The Church Yard'. Use the class ideas to model the poem on the board together. Take care to think carefully about choosing the most descriptive words. Redraft the poem together until the class is happy that it is the final version. Read the class poem aloud together. If the class is particularly pleased with their poem, copy out a version to display on the classroom wall.

Next ask the children to write their own acrostic poems. Collect topics that individuals could use as poem titles from the children themselves.

The children should then draft their own poems, until a final version is achieved. For children who struggle with this activity there is a Writing Support Sheet with a partly completed acrostic. The finished poems could be read aloud, displayed in the classroom or placed in a class anthology.

Acrostic Poems
Grandfather Clock

Name: _____ **Date:** _____

Remember that in an acrostic poem, the first letter of each line spells a word when rea downwards. We use this word as the title of the poem. An acrostic poem does not have to rhyme. Think carefully about adding descriptive words to make your poem more exciting to read. Can you complete this acrostic poem?

Rocking Chair

Real solid oak, shiny dark brown,

Only the finest, of course!

Care, oh such great care taken to make me,

Knowing that I would last a hundred years!

Infants and children love me,

N _____

G _____

Cousins visiting, fight to sit on me.

H _____

A _____

I _____

R _____